CHESTER'S EASIE[ST]

FIRST SOLOS

by Carol Barratt

Exclusive distributors:

Music Sales Limited
8/9 Frith Street,London
W1V 5TZ, England

Music Sales Corporation Distribution Center,
5 Bellvale Road, Chester,
New York 10918,
U.S.A

Music Sales Pty Limited,
120 Rothschild Avenue,
Rosebery, NSW 2018
Australia.

This book © Copyright 1990 by
Chester Music Limited
UK ISBN 0.7119.2291.8
Order No. CH 55989

Art direction by Mike Bell
Cover illustration by Sarah Lenton
Music processed by Barnes Music Engraving Limited
Printed by Caligraving Limited, Thetford, Norfolk.

Chester Music Limited
(A division of Music Sales Limited)

To the teacher:

This book of easy Solos has been carefully written
so that the pupil makes gradual progress from
"alternating hands" to "hands together". It can be
used on its own, or as a supplementary book alongside
Chester's Easiest Piano Course Book 1, and is ideal
for the beginner pianist. These Solos are fun pieces to use
in your teaching, as well as being suitable for
performance in recitals and festivals.

Range:

Right Hand

Left Hand  plus B♭ in the last piece
in the book.

TO THE PUPIL:

This book of Solos is a repertoire book.
Your repertoire is a collection of pieces that **you** can play well–
without too many mistakes!

It's useful to have a good selection of pieces in your repertoire,
as you may often find yourself in front of an audience.
Think of your repertoire pieces as your "party pieces".

Enjoy yourself,

Carol Barratt

1.
ON THE GO

Busily

CH55989

2.
DOZY DO-DO

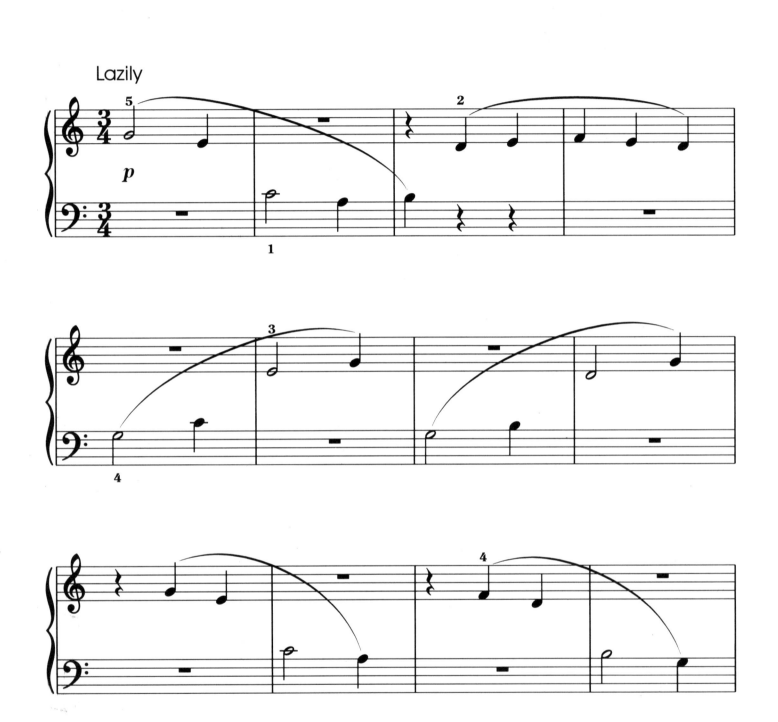

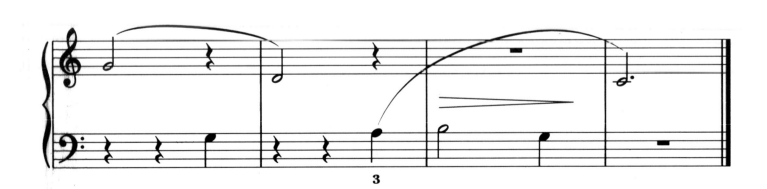

3.
MINI-RAG

Try clapping your hands on the 3rd beat of the bars marked *

4.
PATTERNS

Smoothly

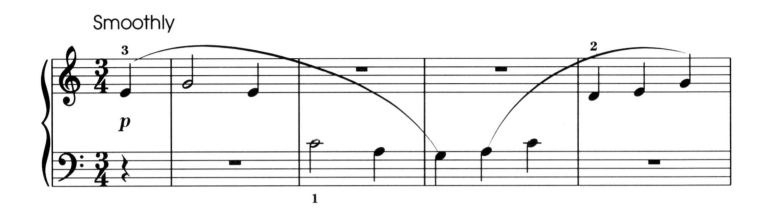

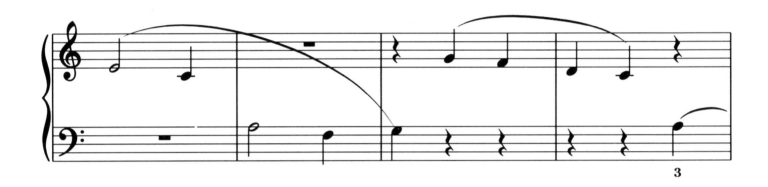

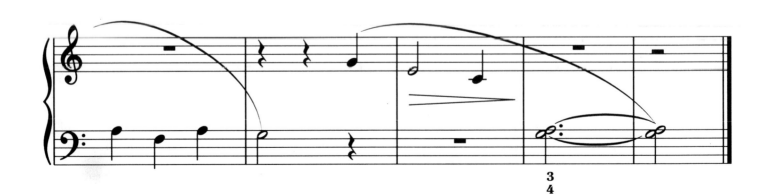

5.
IN A TIZZY!

Crossly!

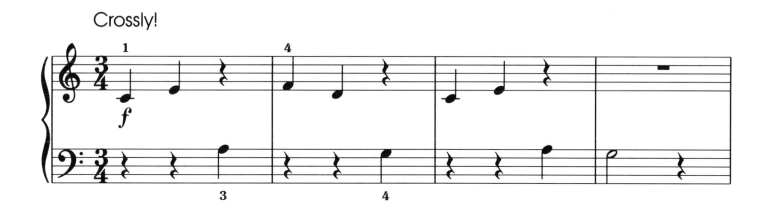

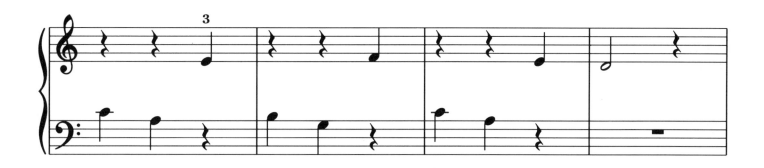

6.
FROGMARCH

Briskly

7.
HANG-GLIDING

8.
JUMPING JACK

With bounce*

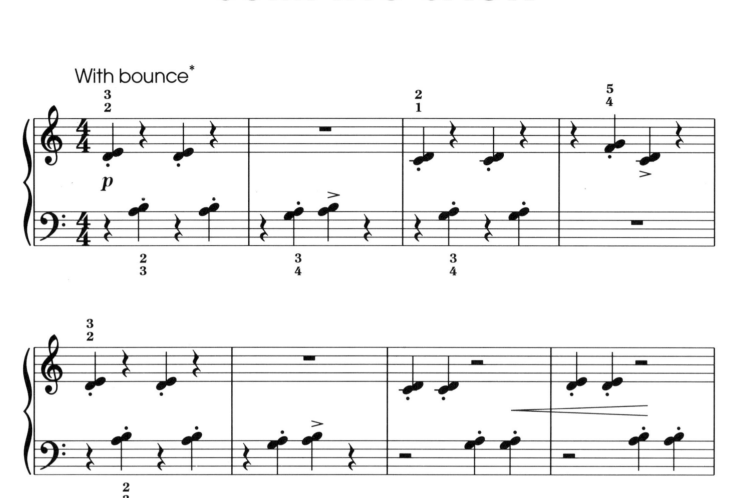

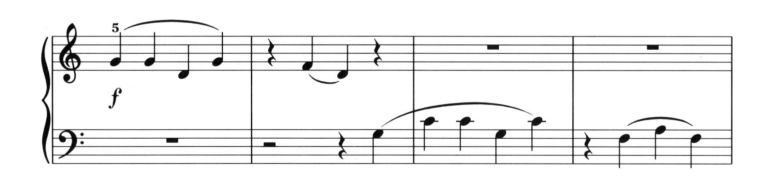

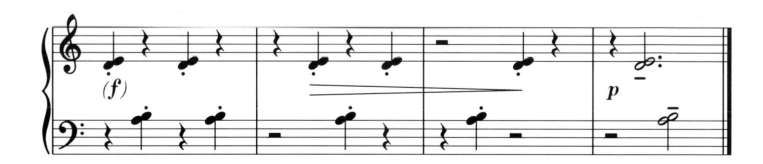

* If you are not yet ready to play a proper *staccato,* just make the chords shorter than usual.

9.
OVER AND ABOVE

Cheekily!

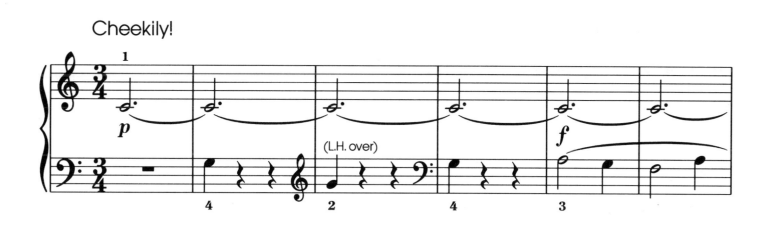

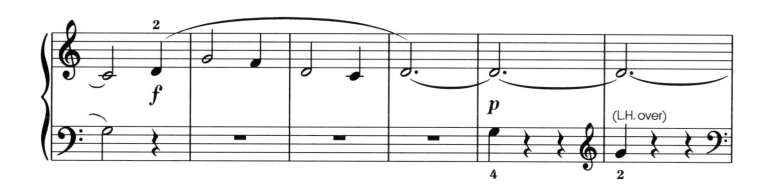

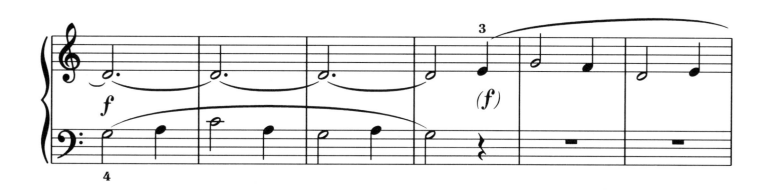

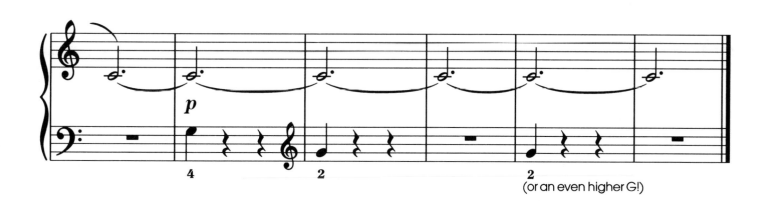

(or an even higher G!)

10.
BILL'S BAGPIPES

Plaintively

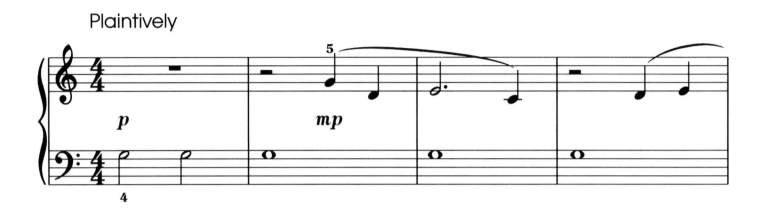

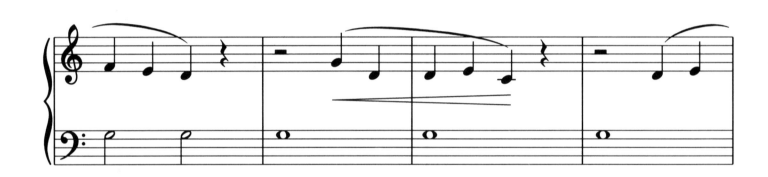

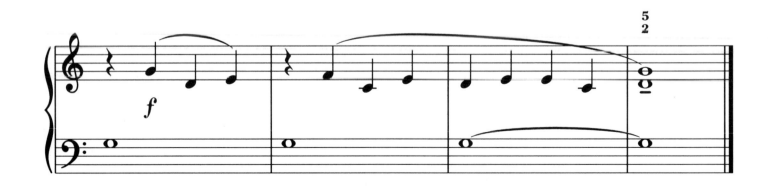

11.
MERRY-GO-ROUND

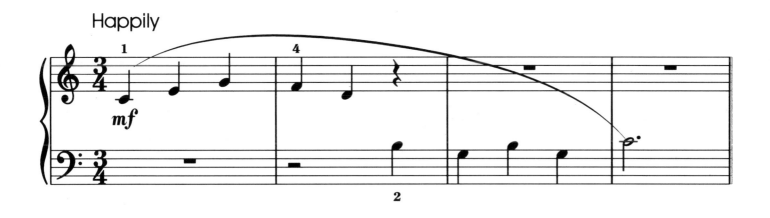

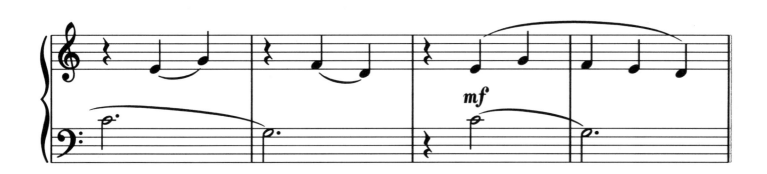

When you can play this piece, try playing it an octave higher than it is written.

12.
FORTUNE COOKIES
(Chinese Music)

Gently flowing

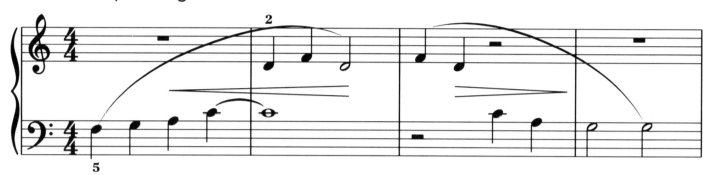

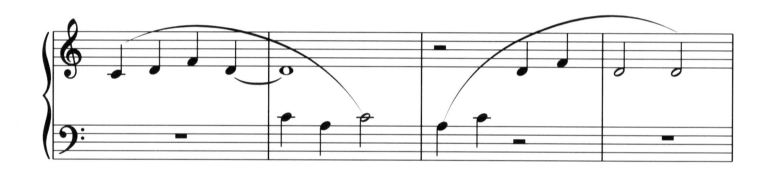

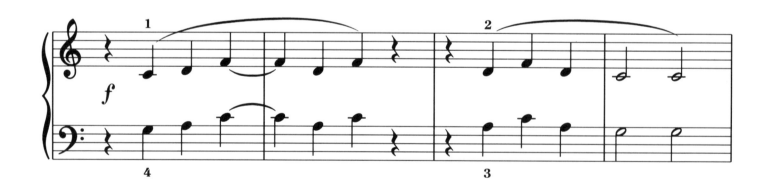

rit. . . . .

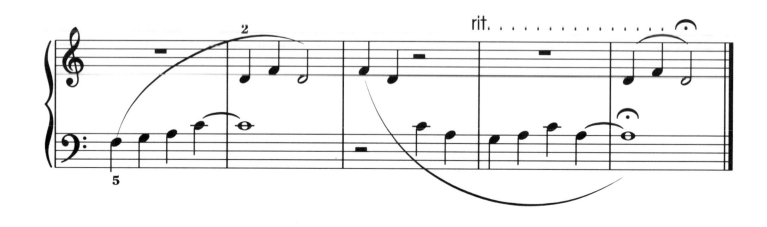

13.
SPELLBOUND

Slowly and magically

14.
CHATTERPIE

(This is another word for Magpie)

Noisily!